# JUST TALK

A PLAY BY
## ELIZABETH SHEPARD

## SCHOLASTIC INC.

New York  Toronto  London  Auckland  Sydney
Mexico City  New Delhi  Hong Kong

## ILLUSTRATIONS BY
## LAURA JACOBSEN

JUST TALK was first published as "A Voice of Her Own"
in *Scholastic SCOPE*® magazine, Vol. 44, No. 7, November 3, 1995.

ISBN 0-439-05695-0

4   5   6   7   8   9   10         23         06   05   04   03

# CHARACTERS

**Sarah Reynolds** - a 16-year-old girl who has been deaf since birth

**Molly** - Sarah's 14-year-old sister

**Richard** - Sarah and Molly's father

**Vicki** - Sarah and Molly's mother

**Adrienne** - Sarah's sign-language tutor

**Judge Wagner**

**Narrator**

*Just Talk* is not a true story. But the idea for the play came from real life.

A few years ago, 15-year-old Sonya Kinney took her father to court.

Sonya was deaf. She learned to communicate by using sign language. But her father would not learn to sign. That made life at home really lonely. Sonya had no one to talk to.

Sonya's sign language teacher, Joanie Hughes, said she would help. Hughes said that Sonya could live with her and her family. There, Sonya would be with other people who spoke her language.

But Sonya's father said no.

Sonya wouldn't give up. She decided to take her father to court. She wanted the court to say it was okay for her to live with the Hughes family.

The main character in *Just Talk* is not Sonya Hughes. It is a made-up character named Sarah Reynolds. Like Sonya, Sarah is deaf. And like Sonya, she has some serious problems at home. . . .

*Sometimes it seems like people just don't want to know what you have to say. . . .*

**ACT 1**

**Sarah** *(signing)*: Hello, my name is Sarah Reynolds. I am 16 years old. I am deaf. I'm the only deaf person in my school. I don't mind, but I do get lonely. I used to have to read lips to understand people. Now I'm learning sign language. It's a lot better than reading lips. But it only works when people can sign back.

**Molly:** I'm Sarah's sister, Molly. I am 14. I can hear, but Sarah is teaching me to sign so that we can understand each other better. It takes time to learn. But I know that Sarah needs people around her who can sign.

**Adrienne:** I'm Adrienne, Sarah's sign-language tutor. I am not deaf, but I have two deaf children at home. Sarah is a great student. She's learning a lot. This year started off great. But then the whole thing with her parents happened.

*Sarah's mother and father don't understand her at all. But what can she do? They're her parents!*

**Act 2**

**Narrator:** Sarah and Adrienne are in a park. They are using sign language to speak with each other.

**Adrienne:** How are you doing today, Sarah? You seem a little sad.

**Sarah:** I'm okay, I guess. Have you spoken with my parents lately?

**Adrienne:** Yes. I called your mother yesterday.

**Sarah:** What did you say?

**Adrienne:** The usual. I told her that I think she should learn sign language. I said it would help you all understand each other better. I also told her I'd teach her and your dad for free. But I've been saying all that for a year now.

**Sarah:** What did she say?

**Adrienne:** She says you two can talk just fine.

**Sarah:** Yeah, right. I try to read her lips, and then

I write her notes. It takes forever.

**Adrienne:** I know it's hard.

**Sarah:** Sometimes she forgets I can't hear. Or she pretends to forget. She turns away and tells me something. I have no idea that she's even talking to me. Then she gets angry with me. It's like I did something wrong.

**Adrienne:** What about your dad?

**Sarah:** He's no help. He works so much that he doesn't feel like speaking *any* language.

**Adrienne:** Sarah, I don't think you should live like this. What if you spoke only Russian and your parents spoke only Chinese? You'd have to learn one language that you *all* could speak.

**Sarah:** I know. I've told Mom that.

**Adrienne:** Well, I've been thinking. What if you lived with me and my family?

**Sarah:** Lived with you?

**Adrienne:** How about it?

**Sarah:** I don't know. It would really hurt my parents and my sister.

**Adrienne:** I know. It's a big step. You should think about it. But we'd love to have you.

**Sarah:** I can't believe you're asking me to be part of your family!

**Adrienne:** You're really part of the family already. My kids love having you around. Their sign language is getting better every day. Ask your parents. You never know. They may like the idea.

What do you think Sarah should do? How would you feel about living at home if you were Sarah?

*Sarah sees a chance for a whole new life. But it means moving away from her parents.*

ACT 3

**Narrator:** It's the next night. Sarah and her family are eating dinner. Molly, Vicki, and Richard are talking. Sarah is trying to read their lips. She can understand only a few words.

**Sarah** *(signing, to Molly)*: What are they saying? Please tell me.

**Molly** *(speaking and trying to sign back)*: I don't know how to sign all the words. But you're not missing much. Dad says he has to work a lot next week. And he says the dryer is broken.

**Narrator:** Richard stamps his foot to get Sarah's attention. She feels the floor shake and turns to him. He points to the butter.

**Richard:** *(loudly)*: Sarah, butter.

**Narrator:** Sarah looks at Molly. Then she passes her father the butter. Her mother snaps her fingers in Sarah's face. This means "sit up

8

straight." Sarah sits up. Then she stares out the kitchen window. She feels hopeless. She takes some paper out of her pocket.

**Sarah** *(writing)*: I wish they'd learn my language. Since they don't want to, I think I should live somewhere else. Adrienne said I could live with her family. I want to go. I need to be around people I can talk to.

**Narrator:** She gives the note to Molly. Molly reads the note and looks at Sarah, surprised. Their parents notice.

**Richard:** What's going on, Molly?

**Vicki:** Molly, what's wrong?

**Narrator:** Molly passes the note to her parents. They read it and become angry.

**Richard:** No! Sarah, you will stay right here with your family. This is where you belong. What's wrong with you?

**Vicki:** Sarah, you're our daughter! We want you to live with us!

**Richard:** Molly, tell your sister that it's out of the question. It's *totally* out of the question!

**Narrator:** Molly tries to sign everything that her

parents said. But she can't keep up. Finally, she gives up.

**Sarah** *(writing)*: I want to be someplace where people can understand me.

**Richard** *(loudly)*: NO!

**Narrator:** He shakes his head.

**Richard:** Listen. We love you. Our family belongs together. That's the end of the discussion. I don't want to talk about this again.

**Narrator:** Sarah is getting more and more frustrated. She grabs the pad and writes another note. This one is short.

**Sarah** *(in the note)*: I HATE it here!

**Vicki:** Sarah, this is your home. You are not going to live with another family.

**Narrator:** Sarah answers in sign language.

**Sarah** *(signing)*: If you cared about me, you would learn sign language.

**Narrator:** Sarah drops her hands. She knows her mother will not understand.

**Vicki:** What? Molly, what is she saying?

**Sarah** *(signing angrily)*: Learn sign language so you can talk with me!

**Vicki:** Richard, I don't understand what she's saying. Can you understand her?

**Richard:** Not really.

**Molly:** She wants you to learn sign language—both of you. Why don't you?

**Richard:** I work. In fact, I work overtime to support this family. It's not easy. I'd like to learn sign language. The truth is that I just don't have the time!

**Molly:** I make time to learn it. Why can't you?

**Richard:** You're just a kid. What else would you do? Lie around and watch TV?

**Vicki:** That's not the point.

**Molly:** Then what is the point?

**Sarah** *(signing)*: I feel lonely all the time. The world moves so slowly when you have to write down every word. You don't know how I feel or what I mean. Nobody here really knows.

**Molly** *(to their parents)*: You don't even know what she's saying. You can't even talk to her. She's lonely.

**Richard:** Everyone is lonely sometimes. Tell her we communicate just fine—in written English.

**Narrator:** Sarah is trying to follow what everyone is saying. She is totally frustrated. She grabs the pad and writes in big letters.

**Sarah** *(in the note)*: I AM LEAVING.

**Narrator:** She runs out of the kitchen. The front door slams. The rest of the family sits in shock.

Do you think a teenager should be able to decide where he or she should live?

*Sarah decides to fight for the life that she wants—in court.*

**Narrator:** It's six months later. Sarah's parents still won't let her live with Adrienne. They still haven't learned sign language, either. Sarah spends most of her free time at Adrienne's house. She only comes home to sleep. She leaves again before breakfast.

One night, she and Molly sit up late. They are talking in sign language.

**Sarah:** Molly, your signing is getting really good. You know a lot more than just the alphabet now.

**Molly:** I've been practicing a lot. And I taught a few friends some signs. We can talk secretly in class. It's better than passing notes.

**Sarah:** Definitely. Now listen, I've got to tell you something. Adrienne and I are taking Mom and Dad to court. We want a judge to say it's okay for me to live with Adrienne and her family.

**Molly:** Wow! Isn't that going a bit too far?

**Sarah:** But Molly, I can't hear. I've never been able to hear, and I never will. I don't mind that. There's a whole community of deaf people. I want to be a part of it.

**Molly:** But we're your family. . . .

**Sarah:** Yes, but my language is American Sign Language. It's a whole other world of signs and symbols and expressions. Mom and Dad don't know anything about it. They can't hear what I have to say or how I say it.

**Molly:** I guess I know what you mean. I feel like I know you better since we started signing. I can tell when you think something matters. Or when you're joking.

**Sarah:** I'm just like everyone else. I want the same things. I feel the same things. But I'm alone here. I shouldn't have to be.

**Molly:** I'll miss you if you move in with Adrienne. I miss you already.

**Sarah:** We'll still see each other a lot. I promise.

*Sarah's future is now in the hands of the judge.*

**Narrator:** It's three months later. Adrienne and Sarah are in court. Sarah has told the judge why she wants to live with Adrienne's family. Sarah's parents have told their side, too.

**Sarah** *(signing to Adrienne)*: I feel guilty. Maybe this is wrong.

**Adrienne** *(signing)*: Be strong, Sarah.

**Sarah** *(signing)*: But I want to do the right thing for us all—not just for me.

**Judge Wagner:** This court shall come to order. Let me remind you all that this case is not about who's right or who's wrong. It's about what's best for Sarah Reynolds.

The main point is this: Vicki and Richard Reynolds have not learned sign language. They have failed to meet their daughter's basic need to communicate.

Adrienne Harris knows sign language. She can communicate with Sarah. She also has proved her ability to care for Sarah.

**Adrienne** *(signing to Sarah)*: Sarah, I think we might have won.

**Judge Wagner:** I believe Sarah will continue to feel lonely and sad in her parents' home. On the other hand, I believe she will grow and learn in Adrienne's home. I am giving Sarah's care and custody to Adrienne Harris.

**Narrator:** Adrienne tells Sarah the verdict. They are very pleased. Behind them, Vicki and Richard are very upset.

**Richard:** I can't believe it!

**Vicki:** You can't just take a child away from her own family!

**Narrator:** Molly catches Sarah's eye and signs "congratulations."

**Sarah** *(signing back):* Thank you.

**Narrator:** Richard snaps his fingers, trying to get Sarah's attention.

**Richard** *(loudly)*: How can you do this?

18

**Narrator:** Sarah signs back to him, but he does not understand.

**Richard:** I don't understand what you're saying. Molly, tell Sarah to write it down.

**Narrator:** Molly tries to hand Sarah a pad and pen. But Sarah won't take it. She keeps signing.

**Vicki:** Adrienne, what's she saying?

**Narrator:** Sarah signs to Adrienne "Please don't interpret for them," and then signs quickly to her mother and father.

**Richard:** What? What are you saying?

**Narrator:** Sarah finally takes the pen and pad and writes them a note.

**Sarah:** When you speak my language, I will be glad to tell you again. Then you'll know what I'm saying. Then you'll know who I am.

---

Did Sarah do the right thing? Do you agree with the judge's decision? Why or why not? Is Sarah's relationship with her parents ruined? What could she do to make sure it isn't?

# SIGN LANGUAGE

Sign language is a language of hand movements. The most common form of sign language in the United States is American Sign Language (ASL).

Many people think that ASL is just English translated into hand movements. That's not true. ASL is its own language—like French or Arabic. Many of the symbols in ASL stand for ideas, not words. For example, there is a single sign used to express the idea "don't care."

ASL began to develop from earlier sign languages sometime around 1860. Like all languages, it continues to change with time.

# American Manual Alphabet

To get a feel for signing, you can start with the basics. Here's the alphabet in sign.

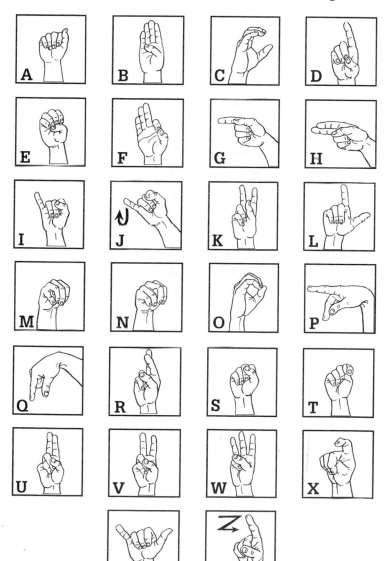